STRANGE BUT TRUE TRIVIA

A QUIZ ABOUT THE THINGS THEY DON'T TELL YOU IN CLASS!

NAT LAMBERT

IMAGINE THAT™

Licensed exclusively to Imagine That Publishing Ltd
Tide Mill Way, Woodbridge, Suffolk, IP12 1AP, UK
www.imaginethat.com
Copyright © 2021 Imagine That Group Ltd
Illustrations copyright © 2021 Shutterstock.com
All rights reserved
0 2 4 6 8 9 7 5 3 1
Manufactured in China

Written by Cassie Parker

ISBN 978-1-80105-019-7

"FOR TRUTH IS ALWAYS STRANGE; STRANGER THAN FICTION."

Lord Byron

QUIZ 1

Alien X Files

7

QUIZ 1

Q1. Area 51 is the common name of a top secret U.S. Air Force facility. Conspiracy theories for the base include it being a site for the storage and reverse engineering of crashed alien spacecraft, and even a place where meetings take place with extraterrestrials! But where in the world is it?

A. Death Valley, California ☐

B. Kodiak Island, Alaska ☐

C. Pearl Harbor, Hawaii ☐

D. Mount Rushmore, South Dakota ☐

E. Groom Lake, Nevada ☒

F. Manhattan, New York ☐

QUIZ 1

Q2. In what year did the world-famous Roswell UFO incident take place?

A. 1937 ☐

B. 1947 ☒

C. 1957 ☐

D. 1967 ☐

E. 1977 ☐

F. 1987 ☐

Q3. One conspiracy theory suggests that aliens visited Earth thousands of years ago and taught humans about technology. Can you name this theory?

A. E.T.B.C. (Extraterrestrial before Christ Theory) ☐

B. Project Antiquity ☐

C. Extraterrestrial Education Theory ☐

D. ET Phone Home Theory ☐

E. Ancient Astronaut Theory ☒

F. UFO Technology Theory ☐

Q4. According to the National UFO Reporting Center, how many UFO sightings were there in 2019?

A. 10 ☐

B. 100 ☐

C. 3,700 ☒

D. 6,889 ☐

E. 100,000 ☐

F. 1,000,000 ☐

Q5. What percentage of Americans believe the government has concealed information about UFOs?

A. 5% ☐

B. 10% ☐

C. 20% ☐

D. 40% ☐

E. 60% ☐

F. 80% ☒

Q6. Published in 1968, Erich von Däniken wrote a book that examined ancient mythologies and legends. He concluded that aliens built the pyramids, and that we mated with the extraterrestrials! What was the name of this best-selling book?

A. Chariots of the Gods? ☒

B. Extraterrestrial Marriage ☐

C. Visitors from Outer Space ☐

D. They Live Among Us ☐

E. Fire in the Sky ☐

F. Aliens in the Family ☐

Q7. When was the earliest known UFO sighting documented?

A. 10,000 B.C. ☐

B. 100 B.C. ☐

C. 1066 ☐

D. 1583 ☐

E. 1864 ☐

F. 1984 ☐

Q8. Which U.S. President once reported seeing a UFO?

A. Donald Trump ☐

B. John F. Kennedy ☐

C. Barrack Obama ☐

D. Jimmy Carter ☒

E. Ronald Reagan ☐

F. Lyndon B. Johnson ☐

Q9. What was the name of the U.S. Air Force's 22-year investigation into the existence of UFOs.

A. The X Files ☐

B. Project Fire Sky ☐

C. Project Blue Book ☐

D. Mission UFO ☐

E. Code 777 ☐

F. Beyond Moon ☐

Q10. Which celebrity is a member or former member of the non-profit organization, the Mutual UFO Network? The organization follows extraterrestrial activity.

A. Tom Cruise ☐

B. Professor Stephen Hawking ☐

C. Dan Aykroyd ☐

D. Demi Moore ☐

E. John Travolta ☐

F. The Rock ☐

Alien X Files Answers

Q1. e. Groom Lake, Nevada

Q2. b. 1947

Q3. e. Ancient Astronaut Theory

Q4. d. 6,889

Q5. f. 80%

Q6. a. Chariots of the Gods?

Q7. b. 100 B.C.
The earliest known report of a UFO sighting was by Julius Obsequens, a Roman writer, in 100 B.C. He claimed to have seen "things like ships" in the sky over Italy. Some people also believe that the Old Testament book of Ezekiel contains a reference to a UFO sighting.

Q8. d. Jimmy Carter
In October 1969, Jimmy Carter observed a UFO in the skies near Leary, Georgia.

Q9. c. Project Blue Book
From 1948–1969 the project investigated hundreds of UFO sightings. The project eventually concluded that there was no evidence of extraterrestrial life.

Q10. c. Dan Aykroyd

QUIZ 2
Monster Mash

QUIZ 2

Q1. The term "zombie" comes from the folklore of which country?

A. Scotland ☐

B. Honduras ☐

C. Chile ☐

D. China ☐

E. Haiti ☐

F. Mexico ☐

QUIZ 2

Q2. The bunyip is a large mythical creature from which people's mythology?

A. American Indian mythology ☐

B. Swedish Norse mythology ☐

C. Australian Aboriginal mythology ☐

D. Mayan mythology ☐

E. Greek mythology ☐

F. West African mythology ☐

Q3. Which enormous sea monster, said to dwell off the coast of Norway, is often represented in the form of a gigantic squid?

A. Behemoth ☐

B. Kraken ☐

C. Megalodon ☐

D. Hydra ☐

E. Basilisk ☐

F. Shonisaurus ☐

QUIZ 2

Q4. Which name is most often given to the fictional island that appears in King Kong films?

A. Skeleton Island ☐

B. Tomb Island ☐

C. Death Island ☐

D. Skull Island ☐

E. Reaper Island ☐

F. Fear Island ☐

QUIZ 2

Q5. Which monster originated from a series of Japanese tokusatsu films of the same name?

A. Tengu ☐

B. Godzilla ☐

C. King Kong ☐

D. Jorogumo ☐

E. Gozu ☐

F. Ryuu ☐

Q6. According to Greek mythology, which fire-breathing monster is usually a lion, with the head of a goat, and a tail that ends with a snake's head?

A. Griffin ☐

B. Cerberus ☐

C. Hydra ☐

D. Centaur ☐

E. Basilisk ☐

F. Chimera ☐

QUIZ 2

Q7. One look at this snake-haired monster from Greek legend would turn you to stone. Who was it?

A. Harpy ☐

B. Chimera ☐

C. Cyclops ☐

D. Minotaur ☐

E. Griffin ☐

F. Medusa ☐

QUIZ 2

Q8. In Arkansas folklore, this tall, shaggy monster has a knack for killing local livestock. What is it called?

A. Big Foot ☐

B. Yeti ☐

C. Mogollon Monster ☐

D. Fouke Monster ☐

E. Slide Rock Bolter ☐

F. Pukwudgie ☐

Q9. The original hound from hell, this pooch had three heads, a tail, and mane of snakes. It guarded the entrance to Hades.

A. Basilisk ☐

B. Kraken ☐

C. Cerberus ☐

D. Argus ☐

E. Minotaur ☐

F. Black Shuck ☐

QUIZ 2

Q10. Commonly described as a hoofed flying creature, tales of this monster are so popular that a professional hockey team is named after the beast.

A. Tampa Demons ☐

B. Oakland Shucks ☐

C. Miami Ogres ☐

D. New Jersey Devils ☐

E. Manhattan Maulers ☐

F. Atlanta Nightcrawlers ☐

QUIZ 2

Monster Mash Answers

Q1. e. Haiti

Q2. c. Australian Aboriginal mythology

Q3. b. Kraken

Q4. d. Skull Island

Q5. b. Godzilla

Q6. f. Chimera

Q7. f. Medusa

Q8. d. Fouke Monster

Q9. c. Cerberus

Q10. d. New Jersey Devils

Most Haunted

QUIZ 3

Q1. Built in 1829 in Philadelphia, Pennsylvania, this famous prison housed criminals including *Al Capone*. Now closed, it is famously haunted with laughter, footsteps, and sightings of ghostly figures. Name the prison...

A. Alcatraz ☐

B. Louisiana State Penitentiary ☐

C. Folsom State Prison ☐

D. Eastern State Penitentiary ☐

E. San Quentin State Prison ☐

F. Attica Correctional Facility ☐

Q2. Lizzie Borden House in Fall Rivers was the scene of the gruesome double ax murders of Andrew and Abby Borden in 1892. The murders were never solved, but you can book a stay at the paranormal house in which U.S. state?

A. Massachusetts ☐

B. Montana ☐

C. New Jersey ☐

D. Pennsylvania ☐

E. Vermont ☐

F. Wyoming ☐

Q3. The bathroom of the Denver & Rio Grande Railroad Depot is said to be haunted by a woman who was hit by a train after her fiancé threw her engagement ring onto the tracks. What color dress is the famous spook said to wear?

A. Red ☐

B. Yellow ☐

C. Black ☐

D. Green ☐

E. Purple ☐

F. Orange ☐

Q4. Hollywood royalty including Audrey Hepburn and Clark Gable have traveled on this haunted liner. Named "The Grey Ghost" during WWII, what is the correct name for this ship that is home to the ghosts of people that died onboard?

A. RMS Carinthia ☐

B. SS United States ☐

C. MSC Bellissima ☐

D. RMS Saxonia ☐

E. SS Europa ☐

F. RMS Queen Mary ☐

Q5. Nettie Dickerson was struck by lightning while standing on a balcony at this famous theater in Charleston. Where might you see her ghost running in a red flowing gown?

A. Dock Street Theatre ☐

B. Kearse Theater ☐

C. Charleston Music Hall ☐

D. Theater 99 ☐

E. Woolfe Street Playhouse ☐

F. Sottile Theater ☐

Q6. In which haunted hotel could you hope not to see the ghosts of an elderly woman in a rocking chair, a bellboy calling "room service", a man who hung raw meat from a chandelier, and two murdered prostitutes?

A. The Grand Hotel, Michigan ☐

B. Sun Valley Lodge, Idaho ☐

C. Hotel Monte Vista, Arizona ☐

D. The Brown Hotel, Kentucky ☐

E. The Golden Lamb Inn, Ohio ☐

F. The Peabody Hotel, Tennessee ☐

Q7. Built in 1820, this is South Carolina's oldest bridge and also its most haunted! The body of a man who died while building the bridge is said to be entombed in its walls. The bridge is also the sight of a fatal accident, and the place where a slave was lynched. What is this macabre bridge called?

A. Poinsett Bridge ☐

B. Hallows Bridge ☐

C. World's End Bridge ☐

D. Deathwatch Bridge ☐

E. Black Bridge ☐

F. Unicorn Rainbow Bridge ☐

Q8. The Lord Baltimore Hotel in Maryland is haunted and then some! Guests have reported being touched by invisible hands in the elevator, and seeing the ghost of a young girl who committed suicide in its halls! But which floor is reportedly the most haunted of all?

A. 3rd ☐

B. 7th ☐

C. 11th ☐

D. 13th ☐

E. 14th ☐

F. 19th ☐

QUIZ 3

Q9. This haunted hotel in Estes Park, Colorado, served as the inspiration behind Stephen King's novel, The Shining. What is it called?

A. The IT Hotel ☐

B. The Stand ☐

C. The Institute ☐

D. The Rose ☐

E. Stanley Hotel ☐

F. The Dome ☐

Q10. On November 13, 1974, Ronald DeFeo Jr. shot and killed six members of his family at 112 Ocean Avenue, Long Island, New York. When a family moved into the property a short while later, they claimed to have been terrorized by poltergeists. In what town is this haunted house?

A. Amity Island ☐

B. Amityville ☐

C. Rhyolite ☐

D. St. Elmo ☐

E. Cahawba ☐

F. Terlingua ☐

Most Haunted Answers

Q1. d. Eastern State Penitentiary

Q2. a. Massachusetts

Q3. e. Purple

Q4. f. RMS Queen Mary

Q5. a. Dock Street Theatre

Q6. c. Hotel Monte Vista, Arizona

Q7. a. Poinsett Bridge

Q8. f. 19th
(The elevator has been known to take guests to the 19th floor without them even touching the button—spooky!)

Q9. e. Stanley Hotel

Q10. b. Amityville

Murder Was The Case!

Q1. Infamous for targeting and cannibalizing men, which serial killer committed his first murder at 18?

A. Ted Bundy ☐

B. Jeffrey Dahmer ☐

C. Ben Stiles ☐

D. Fred Bush ☐

E. John Moore ☐

F. Daniel Lloyd ☐

QUIZ 4

Q2. This serial killer was the inspiration behind Hitchcock's Psycho. Name the man with the mad mom issues.

A. Ted Bundy ☐

B. Alfred Stanley ☐

C. Mad Max ☐

D. Ed Gein ☐

E. Dr. Shipman ☐

F. Fred West ☐

QUIZ 4

Q3. Which notorious London killer stalked sex workers in the late 19th century and was never caught?

A. Mick the Knife ☐

B. Alex the Ax ☐

C. Donald the Scythe ☐

D. Jack the Ripper ☐

E. Jim the Brawler ☐

F. The Phantom ☐

Q4. Which murderer known as "The Killer Clown" gave us circus-performer nightmares long before Stephen King's It?

A. Andy Garcia ☐

B. Chuck Rogers ☐

C. Eric Barton ☐

D. Mark Anthony ☐

E. Norman Bates ☐

F. John Wayne Gacy ☐

QUIZ 4

Q5. *A* ruthless murderer who terrorized California in the 1980s. He received 13 death penalties when he was finally captured.

A. Son of Sam ☐

B. Richard Ramirez ☐

C. Charles Bronson ☐

D. Tom Jones ☐

E. Bret Ellis ☐

F. Stephen King ☐

QUIZ 4

Q6. Can you name the killer who is better known as the "Boston Strangler"?

A. Albert Camus ☐

B. Freddy Krueger ☐

C. Rod Lane ☐

D. Donal Thompson ☐

E. Frederick Charles ☐

F. Albert DeSalvo ☐

QUIZ 4

Q7. Which serial killer better known as the "Son of Sam" terrorized New York in the 1970s?

A. Wes Craven ☐

B. David Berkowitz ☐

C. Ted Bundy ☐

D. James Cordon ☐

E. Albert DeSalvo ☐

F. Robert Englund ☐

Q8. What "Beast" is believed to have murdered over 300 victims?

A. Eric "The Beast" Carlos ☐

B. Luis "The Beast" Garavito ☐

C. John "The Beast" Baptist ☐

D. Dwayne "The Beast" Johnson ☐

E. Paul "The Beast" Smith ☐

F. James "The Beast" Peach ☐

Q9. The way this Californian murderer left his victims earned him his "Trash Bag Killer" title.

A. David Berkowitz ☐

B. David Black ☐

C. Angus Binn ☐

D. Patrick Wayne Kearney ☐

E. John Coltrain ☐

F. Fred Perry ☐

Q10. Which Russian murderer was called the "Chessboard Killer" because he aimed to kill 64 people—one for each square on a chessboard?

A. Alexander Pichushkin ☐

B. Alexander Nevsky ☐

C. Vladimir Putin ☐

D. Nicholas Trotsky ☐

E. Mikhail Bakunin ☐

F. Andrei Rublev ☐

QUIZ 4

Murder Was The Case! Answers

Q1. b. Jeffrey Dahmer
Jeffrey Dahmer is believed to have murdered 17 men between 1978 and 1991.

Q2. d. Ed Gein
Gein's domineering mom controlled his life and, after she died, he built a shrine to her in his home.

Q3. d. Jack the Ripper
The police never found the killer and it remains one of the most famous unsolved serial killer cases in the world.

Q4. f. John Wayne Gacy
The serial killer dressed as a clown for kids' parties, but away from his day job he's believed to have killed 33 victims.

Q5. b. Richard Ramirez
This callous killer was captured by members of the public after a witness on the street identified him.

Q6. f. Albert DeSalvo
He was convicted of killing 13 women and given a life sentence but was killed in prison in 1973.

Q7. b. David Berkowitz

Q8. b. Luis "The Beast" Garavito
Garavito is the world's worst serial killer based on confirmed murders.

Q9. d. Patrick Wayne Kearney
Patrick Wayne Kearney killed 32 people and left their bodies in trash bags on highways.

Q10. a. Alexander Pichushkin
This notorious serial killer is thought to have killed between 49 and 60 people prior to being caught.

Secret Societies

Q1. Which prestigious Ivy League college is home to the even more prestigious secret society, "The Order of Skull and Bones"?

A. Cornell ☐

B. Columbia ☐

C. Princeton ☐

D. Brown ☐

E. Harvard ☐

F. Yale ☐

Q2. Founded in 1119, this group featured prominently in Dan Brown's popular novel, The Da Vinci Code.

A. The White Monks ☐

B. The Night Watch ☐

C. The Watchmen ☐

D. Knights Templar ☐

E. The Crusaders ☐

F. The Searchers ☐

Q3. This club was founded in 1872 by five journalists in San Francisco, and continues to meet in a private grove in Northern California.

A. The Bohemian Club ☐

B. The Bilderbergers ☐

C. Mensa ☐

D. The Rockefeller Society ☐

E. Havana Club ☐

F. Hooters ☐

QUIZ 5

Q4. Thought to be the world's oldest and largest fraternity, this sect started as a group of skilled stone-workers and architects.

A. Freedom Fighters ☐

B. The Freeloaders ☐

C. Food Stampers ☐

D. Foo Fighters ☐

E. The Freight Riders ☐

F. The Freemasons ☐

Q5. "La Cosa Nostra" is another term sometimes used to describe which sprawling crime syndicate?

A. The Mafia ☐

B. The Triad ☐

C. The Media ☐

D. The Bloods ☐

E. The Crips ☐

F. Los Zetas ☐

QUIZ 5

Q6. David Rockefeller founded this group of wealthy, influential people to solve the world's problems.

A. The Unitarian Church ☐

B. The Bilateral League ☐

C. The Trilateral Commission ☐

D. The Hub ☐

E. Quest ☐

F. S.P.A.R.K. ☐

Q7. This secret organization was the original society where all doctors swore an oath to help the sick with no profit to themselves.

A. Order of the Rosy Cross ☐

B. Knights Templar ☐

C. The Order ☐

D. Last Orders ☐

E. Doctors' Orders ☐

F. Order of Time ☐

QUIZ 5

Q8. Founded in Missouri in 1883, members of this society concealed their identities by wearing black horned hoods with white outlines of faces painted on them.

A. The Bison ☐

B. The Bank Robbers ☐

C. Bald Knobblers ☐

D. The Antelopes ☐

E. The Yaks ☐

F. Mountain Goats ☐

QUIZ 5

Q9. In 1997, a secretive group of UFO believers committed mass suicide in San Diego believing they would pass through a portal to a waiting alien spacecraft. What did they call themselves?

A. Aliens Wait ☐

B. Heaven's Gate ☐

C. Starshippers ☐

D. Astral Brotherhood ☐

E. Cosmic Society ☐

F. Comets ☐

Q10. Perhaps the most powerful secret society of them all, this group apparently wants to form a New World Order. Conspiracy theorists claim they already control governments around the globe.

A. The Ivy Club ☐

B. The Breakfast Club ☐

C. The Illuminati ☐

D. The League ☐

E. The Russell Group ☐

F. Founding Fathers ☐

QUIZ 5

Secret Societies
Answers

Q1. f. Yale
Both President George W. Bush and his father, President George H. W. Bush, were members.

Q2. d. Knights Templar
This order eventually grew so powerful it was second only to the Catholic Church.

Q3. a. The Bohemian Club
It's rumored that its members have included every Republican President since Herbert Hoover!

Q4. f. The Freemasons
More than half of the United States' Founding Fathers were Freemasons.

Q5. a. The Mafia

Q6. c. The Trilateral Commission

Q7. a. Order of the Rosy Cross

Q8. c. Bald Knobblers
This society was founded to combat crime on the Ozark region of southwest Missouri.

Q9. b. Heaven's Gate

Q10. c. The Illuminati
No one really knows much about this secret organization or how powerful it is, or isn't!

QUIZ 6

Fears and Phobias

Q1. Xanthophobia is a fear of a specific color, but which one will give sufferers an unwanted fright?

A. Red ☐

B. Orange ☐

C. Green ☐

D. Blue ☐

E. Yellow ☐

F. Indigo ☐

Q2. People who suffer from this phobia wouldn't go to the circus, or enjoy some of Stephen King's famous films either. By what name is a fear of clowns known?

A. Clownophobia ☐

B. Coulrophobia ☐

C. Circusphobia ☐

D. Cosplayphobia ☐

E. Entertainerphobia ☐

F. Comediaphobia ☐

Q3. If a tree falls in an empty forest, does it make a noise? People who suffer from this fear of trees and wooded areas certainly wouldn't be around to ask! What is their phobia called?

A. Turophobia ☐

B. Ombrophobia ☐

C. Hylophobia ☐

D. Coulrophobia ☐

E. Barkophobia ☐

F. Chlorophobia ☐

Q4. Most people suffer with anxiety from this at some point, but what is nomophobia a fear of?

A. Fear of missing out on the latest celebrity gossip. ☐

B. Fear of losing your car keys. ☐

C. Fear of forgetting an important birthday or anniversary. ☐

D. Fear of being without a mobile cell device or beyond contact. ☐

E. Fear of getting a virus on your computer. ☐

F. Fear of ordering the wrong food in a restaurant. ☐

Q5. Ombrophobia is a fear of which perfectly normal weather event?

A. Snow ☐

B. Wind ☐

C. Frost ☐

D. Hail ☐

E. Rain ☐

F. Fog ☐

QUIZ 6

Q6. Eating out at a pizzeria can be difficult for sufferers of turophobia. But what is turophobia a disproportional fear of?

A. Pineapple ☐

B. Cheese ☐

C. Ham ☐

D. Dough ☐

E. Food cut into slices ☐

F. Jalapeño chili pepper ☐

Q7. If you suffer from hippopotomonstrosesquippedaliophobia, what phobia do you suffer from?

A. Fear of long words ☐

B. Fear of hippos ☐

C. Fear of monsters ☐

D. Fear of potatoes ☐

E. Fear of jokes ☐

F. Fear of watering holes ☐

QUIZ 6

Q8. People with this phobia will most likely steer clear of birthday parties, but what is globophobia a fear of?

A. Party games ☐

B. Party hats ☐

C. Cake ☐

D. Balloons ☐

E. Being the center of attention ☐

F. Getting older ☐

QUIZ 6

Q9. Ablutophobia is very common with young children, but it can cause quite a stink as sufferers get older. What is ablutophobia a fear of?

A. Being naked ☐

B. Refuse collection ☐

C. Trash cans ☐

D. Bathing ☐

E. Strong fragrances ☐

F. Flowers ☐

Q10. Fear of peanut butter sticking to the roof of your mouth is known as...?

A. Alektorophobia ☐

B. Pentheraphobia ☐

C. Linonphobia ☐

D. Deipnophobia ☐

E. Omphalophobia ☐

F. Arachibutyrophobia ☐

Fears and Phobias Answers

Q1. e. Yellow

Q2. b. Coulrophobia

Q3. c. Hylophobia

Q4. d. Fear of being without a mobile cell device or beyond contact.

Q5. e. Rain

Q6. b. Cheese

Q7. a. Fear of long words
The American Psychiatric Association doesn't officially recognize this phobia. Instead, hippopotomonstrosesquippedaliophobia is considered a social phobia.

Q8. d. Balloons
Famous sufferers of this phobia include Oprah Winfrey.

Q9. d. Bathing

Q10. f. Arachibutyrophobia
Sufferers of this fear don't dislike peanut butter—they just have a phobia about it sticking to the roof of their mouths!

QUIZ 7

Totally Random Animal Facts!

QUIZ 7

Q1. This unique sea creature's heart is located in its head...

A. Jellyfish ☐

B. Herring ☐

C. Hermit Crab ☐

D. Shrimp ☐

E. Dogfish ☐

F. Anemone ☐

Q2. Can you name the world's lightest mammal? It weighs as much as two peanut M&Ms!

A. Dormouse ☐

B. Bumblebee bat ☐

C. Shrew ☐

D. Weasel ☐

E. Stoat ☐

F. Hummingbird ☐

Q3. Which creature can jump over 100 times its body length?

A. Kangaroo ☐

B. Flying squirrel ☐

C. Cockroach ☐

D. Grasshopper ☐

E. Howler monkey ☐

F. Flea ☐

Q4. This mammal is the only creature that cannot jump, but what is it?

A. Hippo ☐

B. Sloth ☐

C. Rhino ☐

D. Elephant ☐

E. Giraffe ☐

F. Bison ☐

QUIZ 7

Q5. How many insects can an anteater eat in a single day?

A. 1,000 ☐

B. 5,000 ☐

C. 10,000 ☐

D. 20,000 ☐

E. 30,000 ☐

F. 50,000 ☐

QUIZ 7

Q6. What is the only mammal that can fly?

A. Flying squirrel ☐

B. Possum ☐

C. Canadian goose ☐

D. Pterosaur ☐

E. Locust ☐

F. Bat ☐

Q7. Which of these animals can survive for more than two years without food?

A. Elephant ☐

B. Tarantula ☐

C. Dormouse ☐

D. Gecko ☐

E. Rat ☐

F. Goldfish ☐

Q8. *A* "parliament" is the name for a group of which sort of animal?

A. Crows ☐

B. Owls ☐

C. Geese ☐

D. Red deer ☐

E. Penguins ☐

F. Dolphins ☐

Q9. We share 98.4% of our DNA with chimpanzees, but what percentage do we share with slugs?

A. 10% ☐

B. 20% ☐

C. 30% ☐

D. 50% ☐

E. 60% ☐

F. 70% ☐

Q10. How many cows does it take to supply the NFL with enough leather for a year's supply of footballs?

A. 100 ☐

B. 1,000 ☐

C. 2,000 ☐

D. 3,000 ☐

E. 4,000 ☐

F. 5,000 ☐

Totally Random Animal Facts! Answers

Q1. d. Shrimp

Q2. b. Bumblebee bat

Q3. f. Flea
That's the equivalent of a human jumping to the top of a 34-storey skyscraper!

Q4. d. Elephant
Unlike most mammals, the bones in elephant legs are all pointed downward, which means they don't have the "spring" required to push off the ground.

Q5. e. 30,000

Q6. f. Bat

Q7. b. Tarantula

Q8. b. Owls

Q9. f. 70%

Q10. d. 3,000

Ludicrous Laws!

QUIZ 8

Q1. In which U.S. State is it illegal to whisper in someone's ear if they are hunting for moose?

A. Alabama ☐

B. Oregon ☐

C. New Jersey ☐

D. Alaska ☐

E. Indiana ☐

F. Ohio ☐

Q2. Putting an American flag on top of a bar of soap used to get you into trouble in this state. Which one?

A. Montana

B. Arkansas

C. Florida

D. Nevada

E. California

F. Maryland

Q3. In Wisconsin it was illegal to sell this popular dessert without a side of cheese. What was the dessert?

A. Blueberry muffin ☐

B. Apple pie ☐

C. Ice cream ☐

D. Sorbet ☐

E. Pecan pie ☐

F. Cheesecake ☐

QUIZ 8

Q4. In which state did it used to be illegal to serve wine in teacups?

A. Kansas ☐

B. Kentucky ☐

C. Maine ☐

D. Louisiana ☐

E. Michigan ☐

F. New Hampshire ☐

Q5. In Missouri it used to be illegal to deface which item of food packaging?

A. OJ carton ☐

B. Milk carton ☐

C. Egg box ☐

D. Cereal box ☐

E. Cola bottle ☐

F. Grocery bag ☐

QUIZ 8

Q6. Which state used to issue $50 fines to anyone caught hammering a nail into a tree?

A. Maryland ☐

B. Arizona ☐

C. Mississippi ☐

D. Oklahoma ☐

E. Illinois ☐

F. Kentucky ☐

QUIZ 8

Q7. In which state must pickles be able to bounce in order to gain legal pickle status?

A. Delaware ☐

B. Connecticut ☐

C. Hawaii ☐

D. Oklahoma ☐

E. South Carolina ☐

F. Iowa ☐

QUIZ 8

Q8. In which state is it forbidden to cross state lines with a bird on your head?

A. Delaware ☐

B. Nebraska ☐

C. Vermont ☐

D. Georgia ☐

E. Minnesota ☐

F. Virginia ☐

QUIZ 8

Q9. In Utah, it used to be illegal to carry this musical instrument in a paper bag. Which instrument was it?

A. Banjo ☐

B. Recorder ☐

C. Ukulele ☐

D. Violin ☐

E. Flute ☐

F. Maracas ☐

Q10. In which State was it formerly illegal to carry ice cream in your back pocket?

A. North Dakota ☐

B. New York ☐

C. Alabama ☐

D. Rhode Island ☐

E. New Mexico ☐

F. Pennsylvania ☐

QUIZ 8

Ludicrous Laws!
Answers

Q1. d. Alaska

Q2. d. Nevada

Q3. b. Apple pie

Q4. a. Kansas

Q5. b. Milk carton

Q6. a. Maryland

Q7. b. Connecticut

Q8. e. Minnesota

Q9. d. Violin

Q10. c. Alabama

Strange But True At The Movies

Q1. If you are eagle-eyed, you will see a cup from this well-known coffee chain in virtually every scene from the movie, Fight Club. Which chain is it?

A. Dunkin' ☐

B. Tim Hortons ☐

C. Starbucks ☐

D. Caribou Coffee ☐

E. Dutch Bros. Coffee ☐

F. Peet's Coffee ☐

Q2. Where does the complicated-looking green code that appears in The Matrix movies come from?

A. It's a randomly-generated computer algorithm. ☐

B. It's a code based on the cipher devised by the Roman Emperor, Julius Caesar. ☐

C. It's a unique set of numbers based on the ages of the cast members. ☐

D. It's based on symbols featured in a sushi cookbook. ☐

E. It is the sum of all the money spent on costume design in each movie. ☐

F. It is the sum of all the money that Keanu Reeves has donated to charity. ☐

Q3. Which James Bond actor wore a wig in every movie that he played 007?

A. Daniel Craig ☐

B. Roger Moore ☐

C. Timothy Dalton ☐

D. George Lazenby ☐

E. Pierce Brosnan ☐

F. Sean Connery ☐

Q4. The sound of these mating animals was used to simulate communicating Velociraptors in Jurassic Park. Which amorous animals did the sound engineer use?

A. Chihuahuas ☐

B. Geese ☐

C. Tortoises ☐

D. Blue whales ☐

E. Porcupines ☐

F. Golden eagles ☐

QUIZ 9

Q5. More at home in a galaxy far, far away, which robot (or robots) appeared in hieroglyphics in the movie Indiana Jones?

A. The Terminator ☐

B. Johnny 5 ☐

C. Optimus Prime ☐

D. R2-D2 and C-3PO ☐

E. Baymax ☐

F. Roy Batty ☐

QUIZ 9

Q6. Now Hollywood royalty, which struggling actor had to sell his dog in order to buy food before he made it on the big screen?

A. Tom Cruise ☐

B. Bruce Willis ☐

C. Sylvester Stallone ☐

D. Nicholas Cage ☐

E. Robert De Niro ☐

F. John Travolta ☐

Q7. Back in the day, the Motion Picture Production Code banned flushing toilets from being seen on the big screen. Which movie broke this censorship taboo, and went on to achieve cult status?

A. *A Nightmare on Elm Street* ☐

B. Bladerunner ☐

C. Psycho ☐

D. Gone with the Wind ☐

E. *A Clockwork Orange* ☐

F. Big Wednesday ☐

Q8. *A* mask based on which space traveling hero was used by Michael Myers in the Halloween horror movies...

A. Jean-Luc Picard ☐

B. Buck Rogers ☐

C. Flash Gordon ☐

D. Captain Kirk ☐

E. Luke Skywalker ☐

F. Han Solo ☐

QUIZ 9

Q9. On which A-list Hollywood actor was the animated Disney character of Aladdin modeled?

A. Al Pacino ☐

B. Leonardo DiCaprio ☐

C. Ben Affleck ☐

D. Tom Cruise ☐

E. Robert Downey Jr. ☐

F. George Clooney ☐

Q10. How was the alien language created in the sci-fi action thriller, District 9?

A. Using sound recordings of solar winds. ☐

B. Capturing the echo location calls of a pod of orcas. ☐

C. Distorting NYC traffic noise. ☐

D. With experimental percussion instruments. ☐

E. Using an old electronic keyboard. ☐

F. Rubbing pumpkins together. ☐

QUIZ 9

Strange But True At The Movies Answers

Q1. c. Starbucks

Q2. d. It's based on symbols featured in a sushi cookbook.

Q3. f. Sean Connery

Q4. c. Tortoises

Q5. d. R2-D2 and C-3PO

Q6. c. Sylvester Stallone
His dog was called Butkus and he got $40 for him. He eventually bought Butkus back, and even gave him a starring role in the first Rocky movie!

Q7. c. Psycho

Q8. d. Captain Kirk (played by William Shatner)

Q9. d. Tom Cruise

Q10. f. Rubbing pumpkins together

QUIZ 10

Weird Food Facts

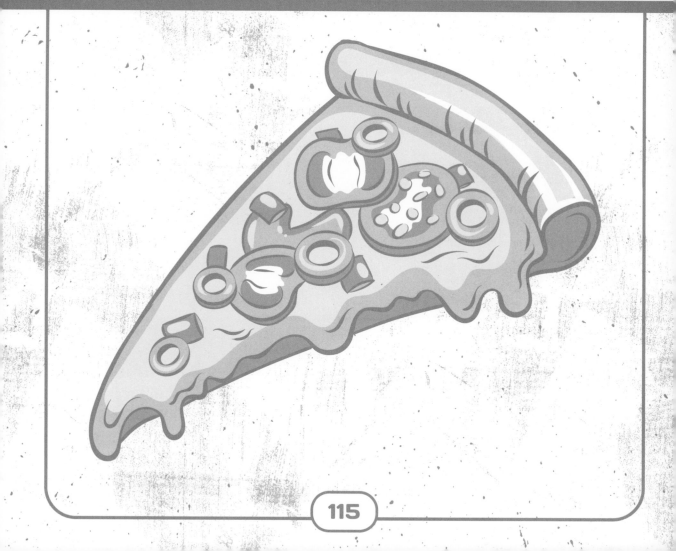

QUIZ 10

Q1. This mealtime staple was invented by a gambling addict who didn't want to leave the table to eat. What is it?

A. Samosa ☐

B. Sandwich ☐

C. Taco ☐

D. Burrito ☐

E. Crêpe ☐

F. Onion bahji ☐

QUIZ 10

A. Poland ☐

B. Germany ☐

C. Chile ☐

D. Peru ☐

E. Kazakhstan ☐

F. Russia ☐

Q3. What percentage of the world's hazelnuts are used to make the Nutella brand of chocolate spread?

A. 5% ☐

B. 10% ☐

C. 15% ☐

D. 20% ☐

E. 25% ☐

F. 30% ☐

Q4. What food did astronaut John Young smuggle into space in 1965?

A. M&Ms

B. Slice of pecan pie

C. KFC bucket

D. 9 oz. steak

E. Corned beef sandwich

F. Skittles

QUIZ 10

Q5. On the 4th of July, we eat so much of this food that it would stretch from Washington DC to Los Angeles five times over!

A. Bananas ☐

B. Celery ☐

C. Hotdogs ☐

D. Pickles ☐

E. Candy bars ☐

F. Corn ☐

Q6. Castoreum, which is used as a substitute vanilla flavoring, is actually taken from the anal glands (yuk!) of which animal?

A. Beaver ☐

B. Mice ☐

C. Rabbits ☐

D. Cockroach ☐

E. Rattlesnake ☐

F. Humpback whale ☐

QUIZ 10

Q7. Which of the following foods never spoils?

A. Milk ☐

B. Jell-O ☐

C. Honey ☐

D. Peanut butter ☐

E. Strawberry jelly ☐

F. Ice cream ☐

Q8. Blibber-Blubber was the first of its kind in 1906, but what is it?

A. Jell-O ☐

B. Jelly bean ☐

C. Meat sauce ☐

D. Bubble gum ☐

E. Breakfast cereal ☐

F. Licorice ☐

Q9. How hot does it have to be to fry an egg on the sidewalk?

A. 100°F ☐

B. 112°F ☐

C. 127°F ☐

D. 133°F ☐

E. 143°F ☐

F. 158°F ☐

QUIZ 10

Q10. What is the most stolen food in the world?

A. Cheese ☐

B. Candy ☐

C. Chicken soup ☐

D. Potato chips ☐

E. Cookies ☐

F. Peanuts ☐

QUIZ 10

Weird Food Facts Answers

Q1. b. Sandwich
The Earl of Sandwich is attributed with inventing the sandwich during a 24-hour card game.

Q2. f. Russia
Before 2011, beer and any alcoholic beverage under 10% ABV was classified as a soft drink.

Q3. e. 25%

Q4. e. Corned beef sandwich

Q5. c. Hotdogs

Q6. a. Beaver

Q7. c. Honey

Q8. d. Bubble gum

Q9. f. 158°F

Q10. a. Cheese
Around 4% of all the cheese made in the world gets stolen.

QUIZ 11

Totally
Random Quiz

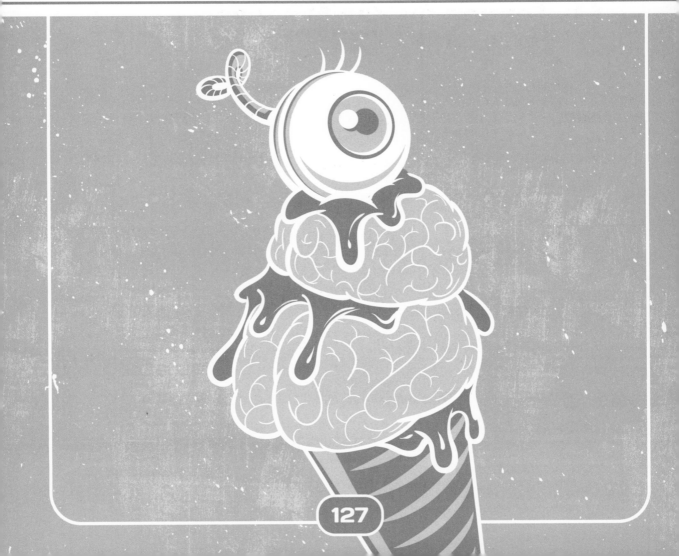

QUIZ 11

Q1. What was the first video ever uploaded to YouTube?

A. Hello from home by Amy Teller ☐

B. Testing by Zak Nicholls ☐

C. Me and my dog by Katie Price ☐

D. Me at the zoo by Jawed Karim ☐

E. My cat rocks! by Patrick Heron ☐

F. Cat chases dog by Imogen Sparks ☐

Q2. How much did Nike pay for the world-famous swoosh logo?

A. $35 ☐

B. $3,500 ☐

C. $35,000 ☐

D. $350,000 ☐

E. $3,500,000 ☐

F. $35,000,000 ☐

Q3. By what name is superhero Hank McCoy better known?

A. Ant Man ☐

B. Iron Man ☐

C. Spiderman ☐

D. Beast ☐

E. Deadpool ☐

F. The Hulk ☐

Q4. Which former U.S. President was inducted into the National Wrestling Hall of Fame in 1992?

A. Donald Trump ☐

B. Abraham Lincoln ☐

C. Bill Clinton ☐

D. George H. W. Bush ☐

E. Barack Obama ☐

F. Dwight D. Eisenhower ☐

Q5. What was the name of the ship found floating in the middle of the Atlantic Ocean on December 4 1872 with no crew?

A. Mary Rose ☐

B. Santa Maria ☐

C. Mary Celeste ☑

D. The Flying Dutchman ☐

E. São Martinho ☐

F. Holyghost de la Tour ☐

Q6. Invented in 1924, how many Dum Dums candies are made every day?

A. 1 million ☐

B. 2 million ☐

C. 4 million ☐

D. 8 million ☐

E. 10 million ☐

F. 12 million ☐

Q7. *A* "flamboyance" is a word used to describe a group of which type of bird?

A. Parrots ☐

B. Emus ☐

C. Flamingos ☐

D. Peacocks ☐

E. Kingfishers ☐

F. Toucans ☐

Q8. Introduced as "Fairy Floss" by a dentist at the 1904 World's Fair, by what name is this product now known?

A. Dental floss ☐

B. Cotton candy ☐

C. Marshmallow ☐

D. Cream soda ☐

E. Chewing gum ☐

F. Cotton wool ☐

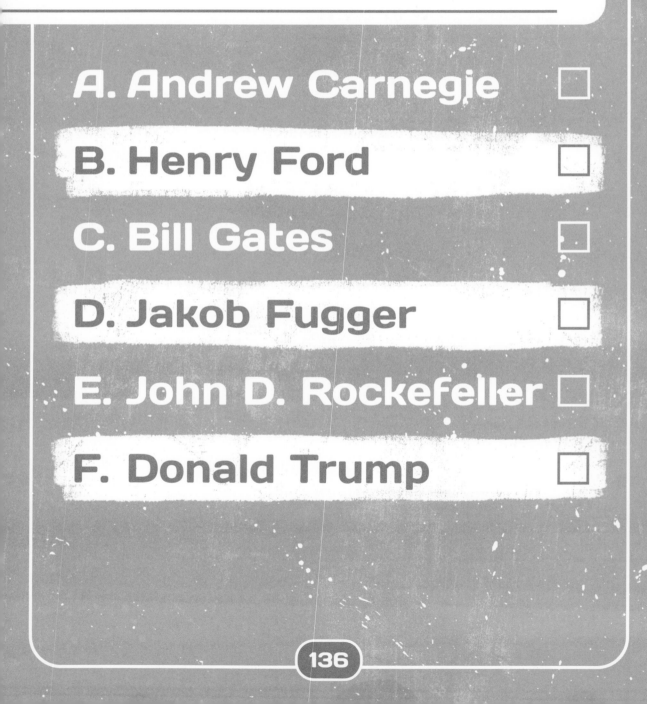

QUIZ 11

Q9. Who was the first person to reach a nominal personal fortune of US$1 billion?

A. Andrew Carnegie ☐

B. Henry Ford ☐

C. Bill Gates ☐

D. Jakob Fugger ☐

E. John D. Rockefeller ☐

F. Donald Trump ☐

Q10. What color is Coca Cola before the coloring is added?

A. Red ☐

B. Clear ☐

C. Green ☐

D. Yellow ☐

E. Purple ☐

F. Blue ☐

QUIZ 11

Q11. Which animal tastes with their feet?

A. Sloth ☐

B. Koala ☐

C. Butterfly ☐

D. Ladybug ☐

E. Gecko ☐

F. Kangaroo ☐

Q12. What famous film is referenced in Britney Spears' Oops I Did It Again?

A. Star Wars: The Empire Strikes Back ☐

B. Cheaper by the Dozen ☐

C. Titanic ☐

D. Home Alone 2 ☐

E. American Pie 2 ☐

F. Alien vs. Predator ☐

Q13. Which animal is responsible for the most human deaths each year?

A. Crocodile ☐

B. Hippo ☐

C. Snake ☐

D. Mosquito ☐

E. Shark ☐

F. Tiger ☐

Q14. Invented in the 12th century in China, what was the original purpose of sunglasses?

A. To protect the eyes from flying debris during the monsoon season. ☐

B. To hide signs of under-eye tiredness. ☐

C. To protect the identity of the wearer. ☐

D. To prevent long beards from blowing into the eyes. ☐

E. To mask the emotions of judges when questioning witnesses. ☐

F. To allow people to see their reflection whilst talking to the wearer. ☐

Totally Random Quiz Answers

Q1. d. Me at the zoo by Jawed Karim

Q2. a. $35
Unsure about how much to ask for, graphic design student Carolyn Davidson asked for just $35 for her design in the 1960s.

Q3. d. Beast
Beast is a fictional superhero in comic books published by Marvel Comics.

Q4. b. Abraham Lincoln
President Abraham Lincoln was a keen wrestler with long limbs and was only defeated once in roughly 300 matches!

Q5. c. Mary Celeste
The ship was seaworthy, its stores and supplies were untouched, but not a soul was onboard.

Q6. f. 12 million

Q7. c. Flamingos

Q8. b. Cotton candy

Q9. e. John D. Rockefeller
By the time of his death in 1937, estimates place his net worth in the range of US$300 billion to US$400 billion.

Q10. c. Green

Q11. c. Butterfly

Q12. c. Titanic

Q13. d. Mosquito
Mosquitoes suck blood and transmit viruses from person to person. They are responsible for over 750,000 human deaths each year.

Q14. e. To mask the emotions of judges when questioning witnesses.